FUN AND CHALLENGING
MAZES
FOR KIDS 8-12

AN AMAZING MAZE ACTIVITY BOOK FOR KIDS

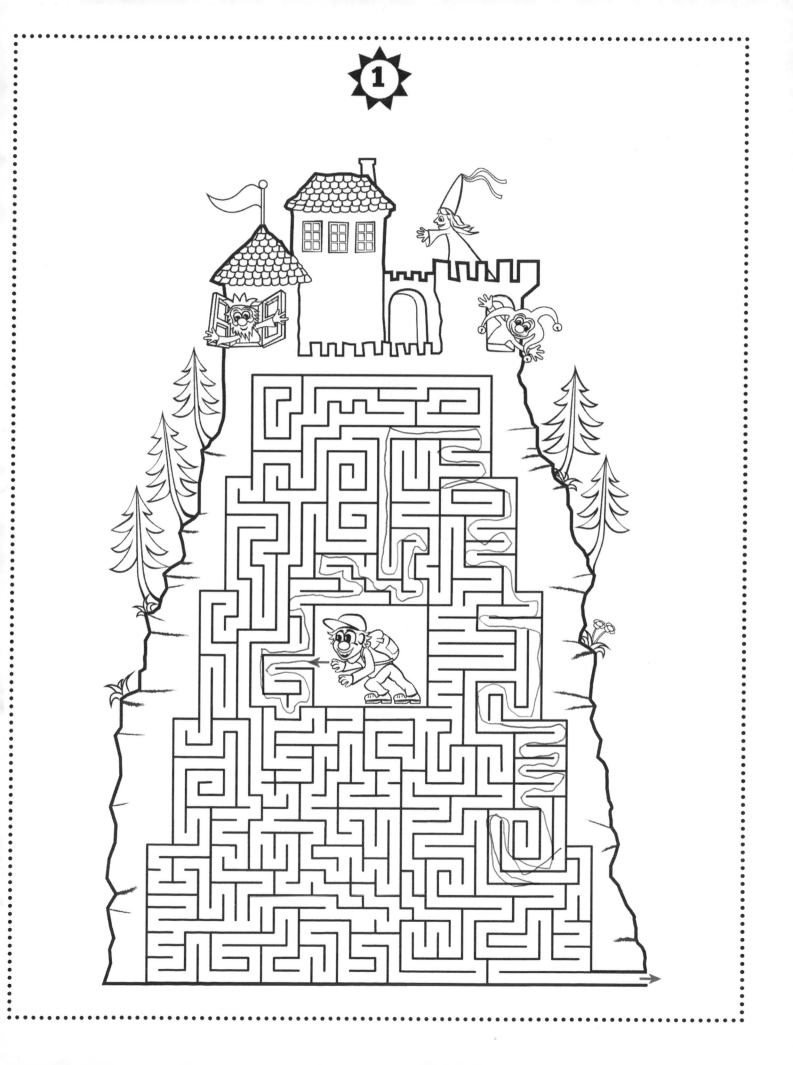

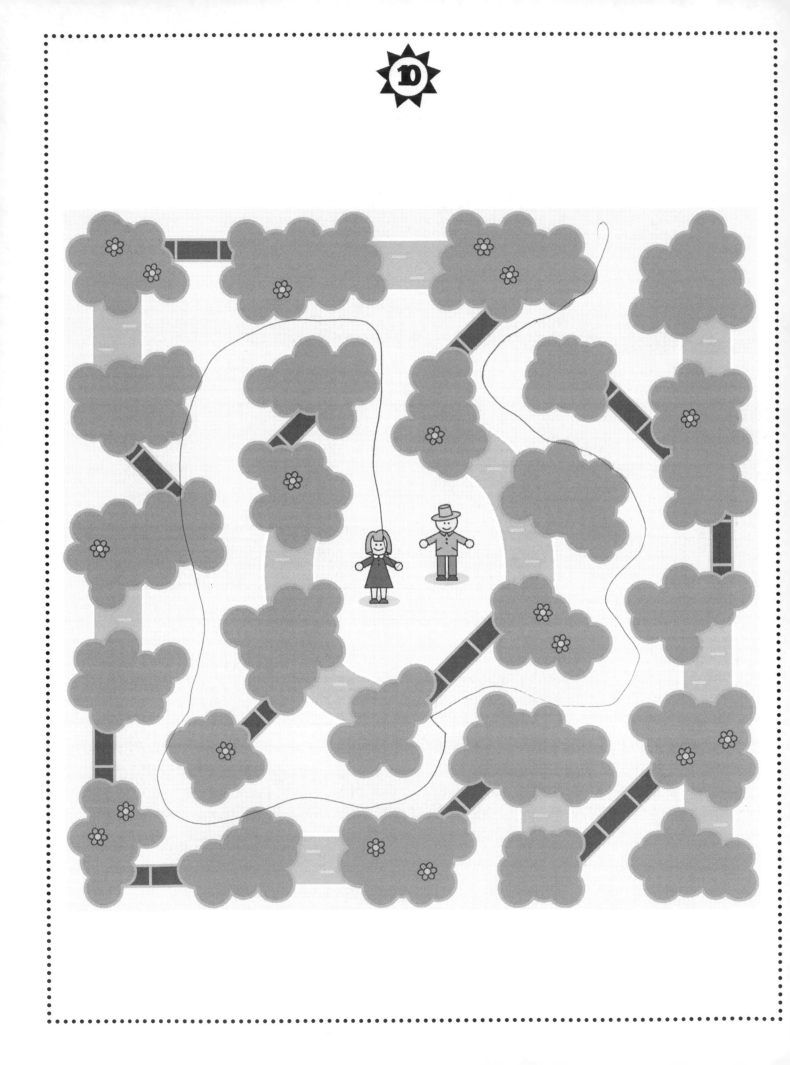

17

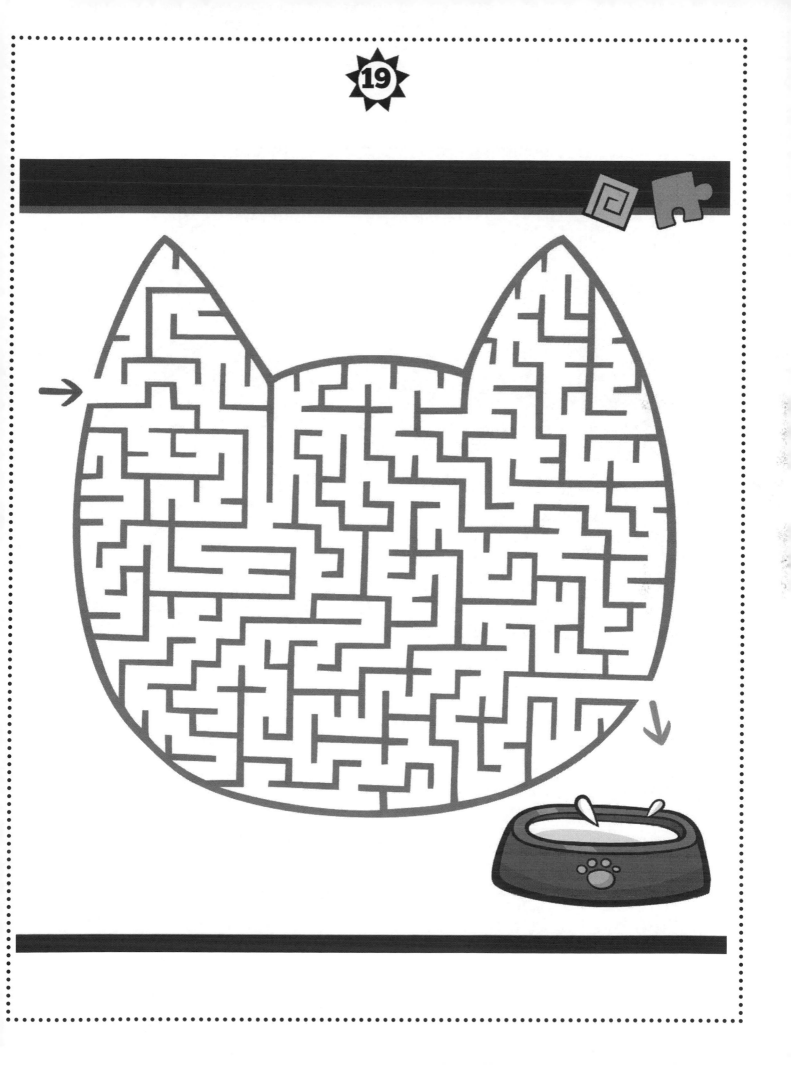

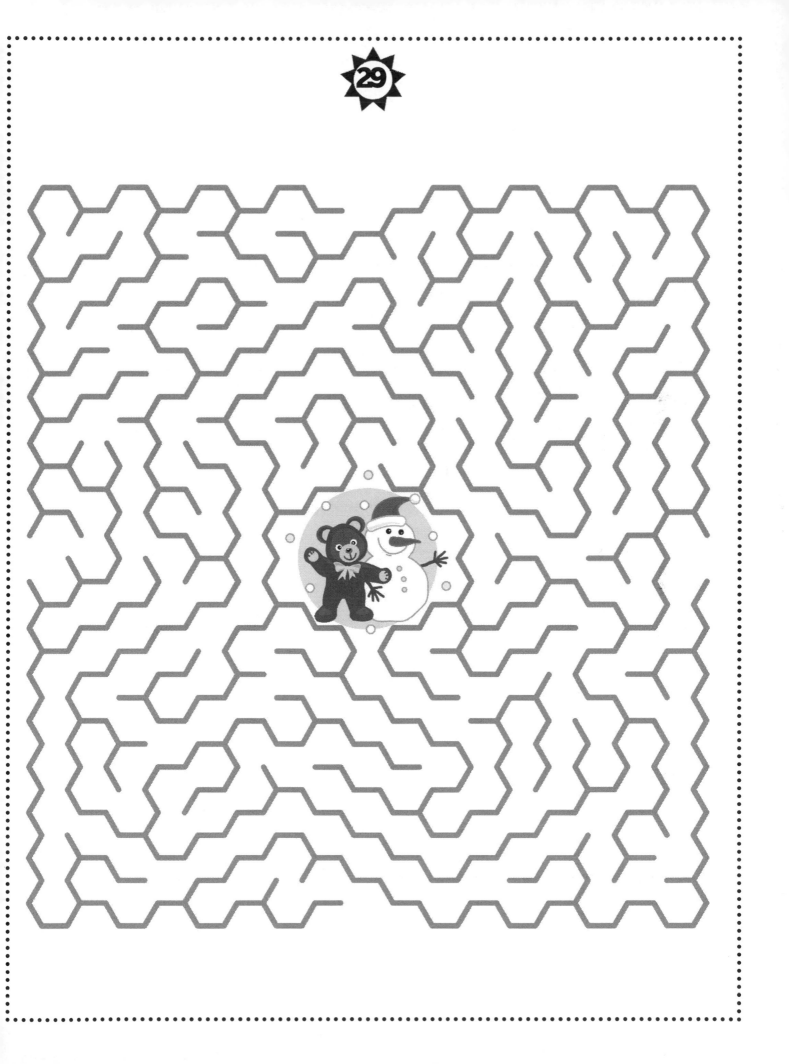

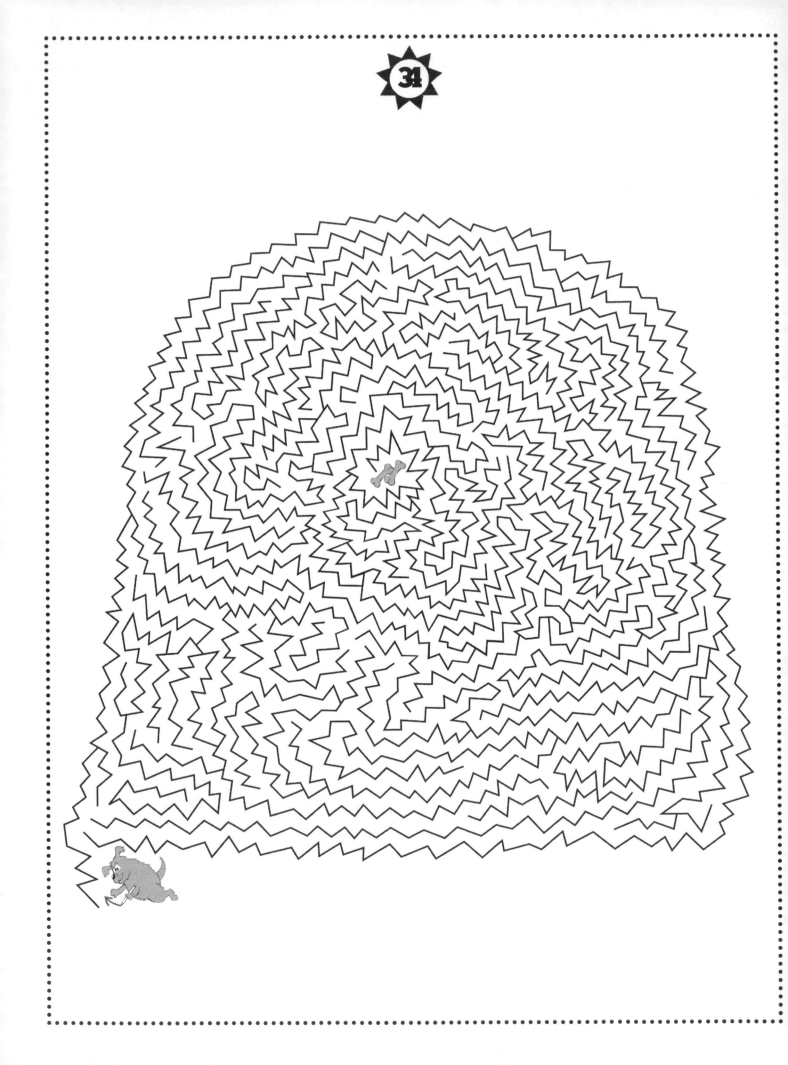

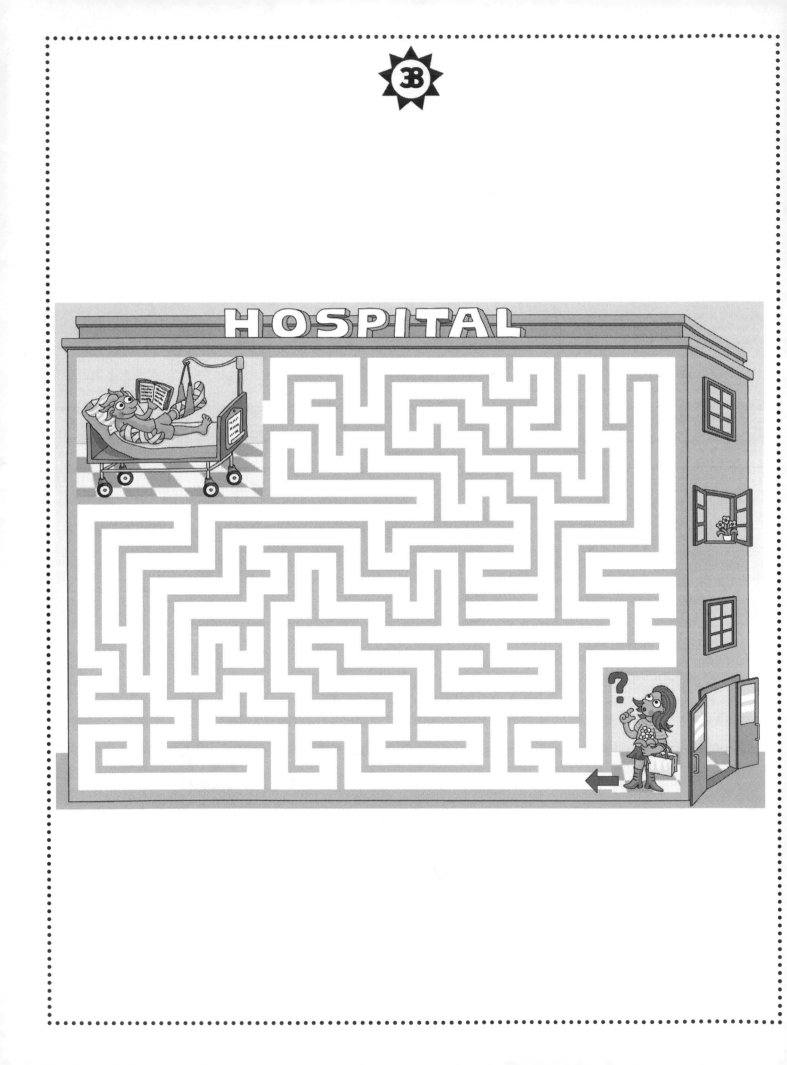

39

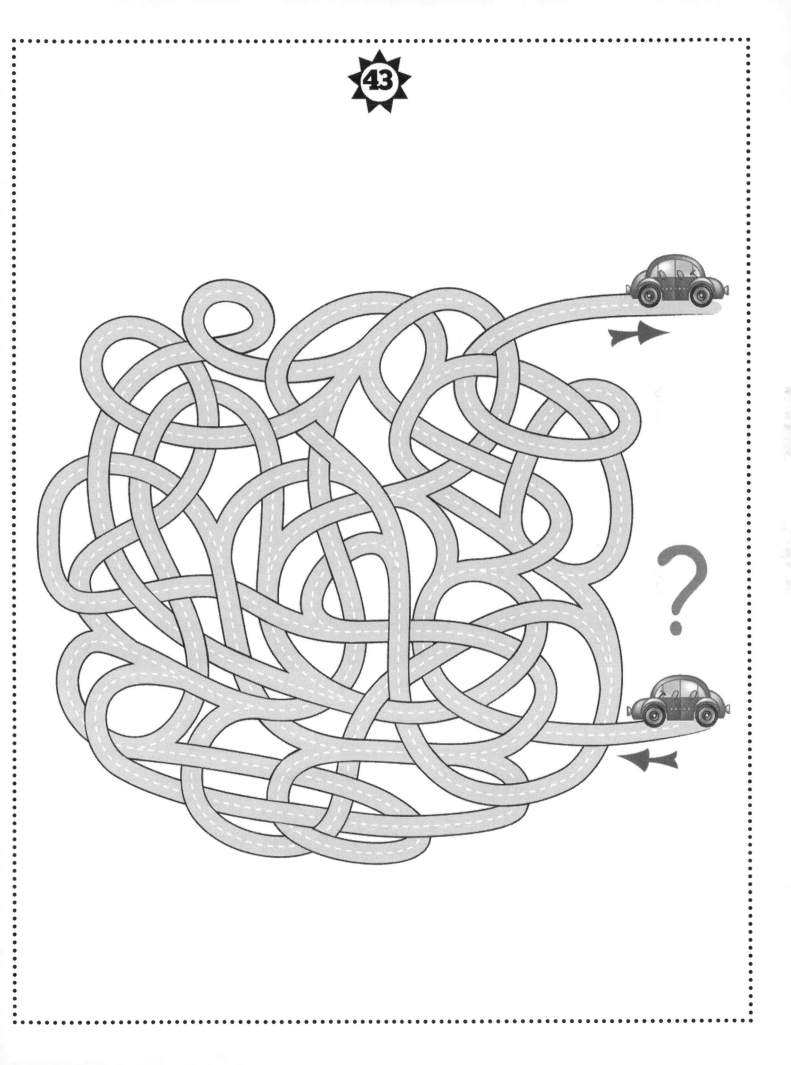

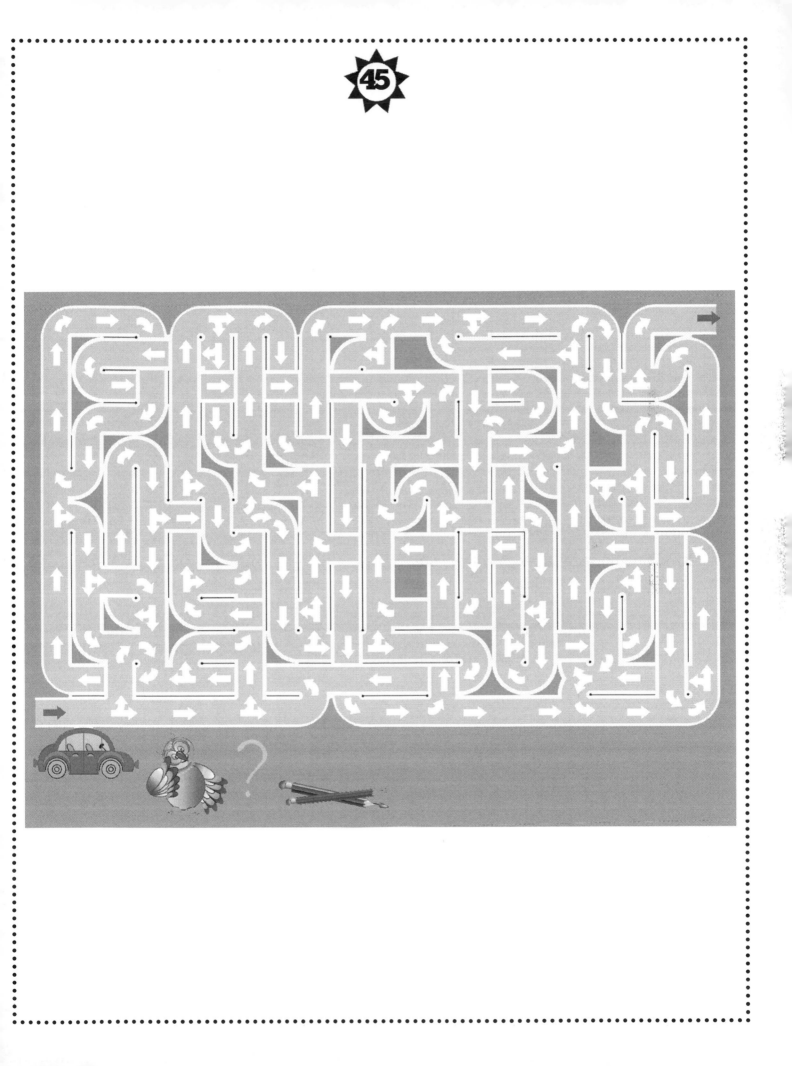

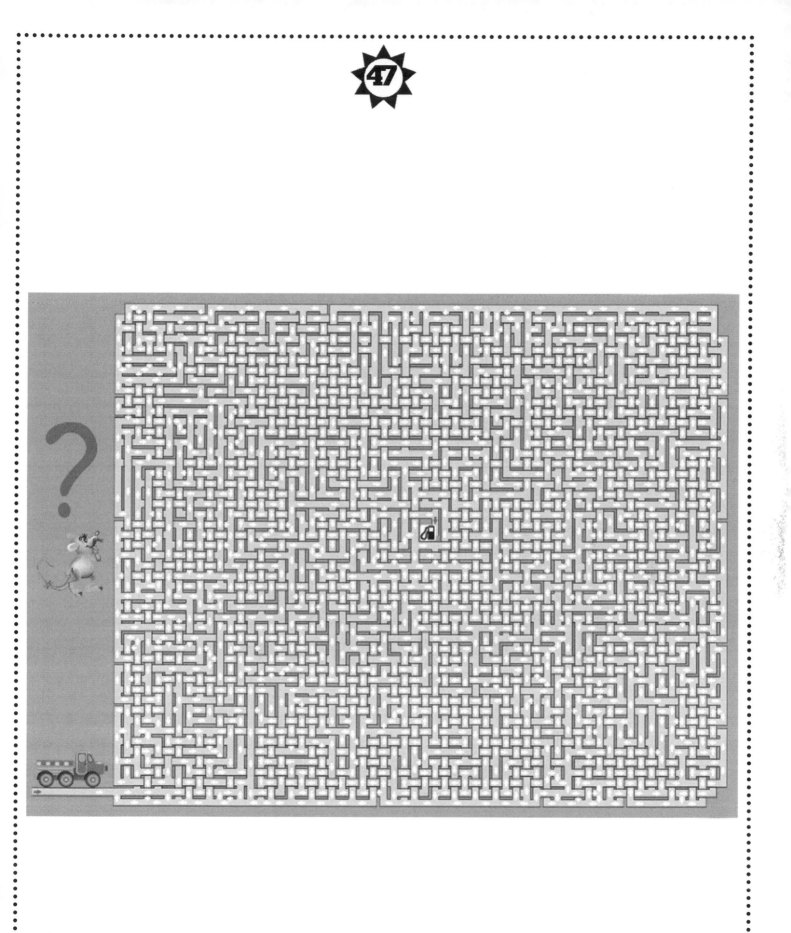

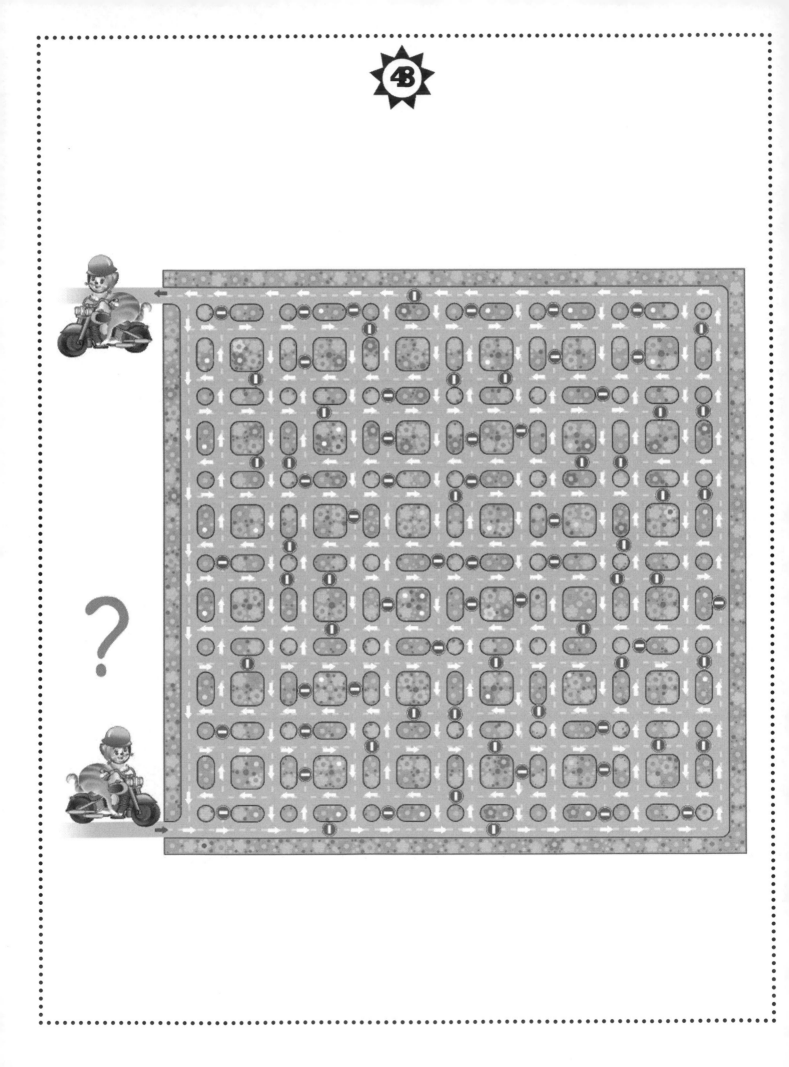

The key that you have can open only one locked door.
Can you get out of the maze?

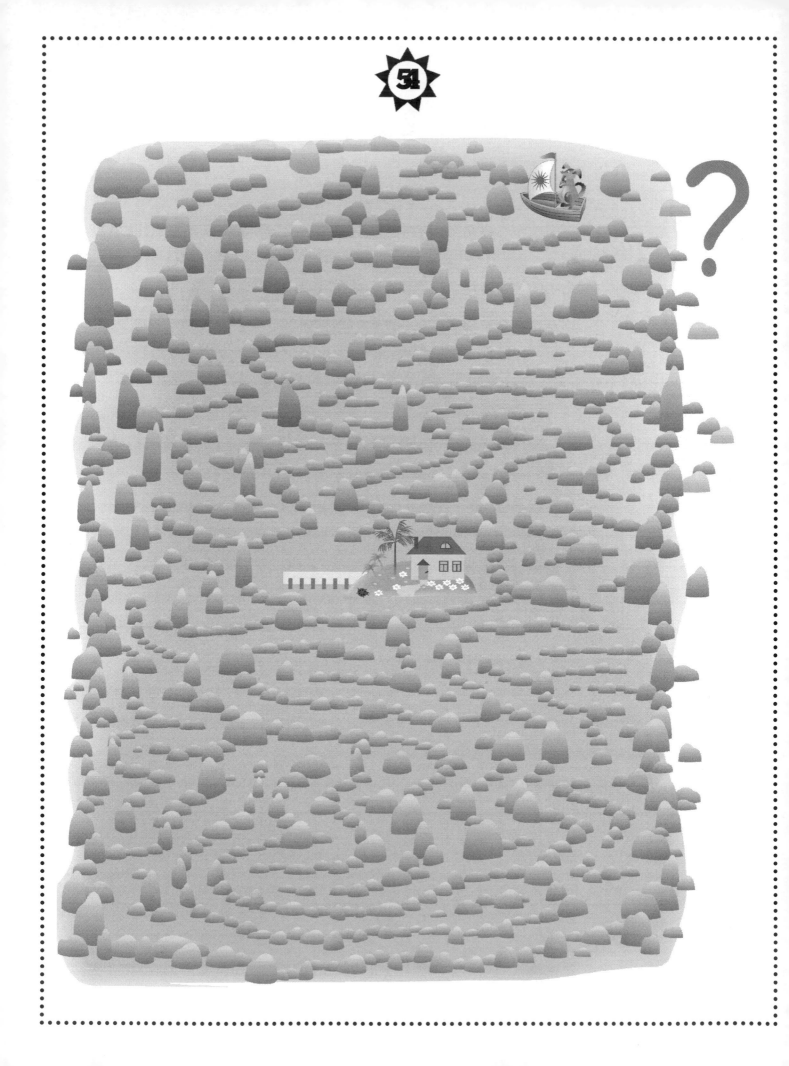

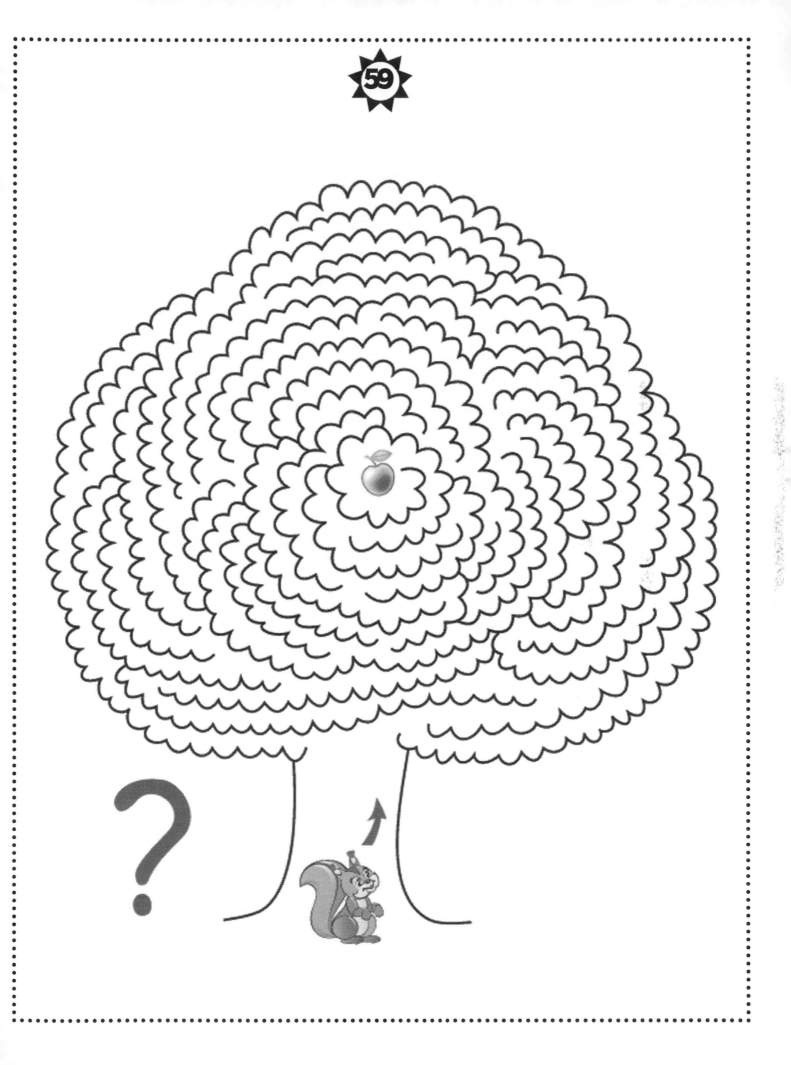

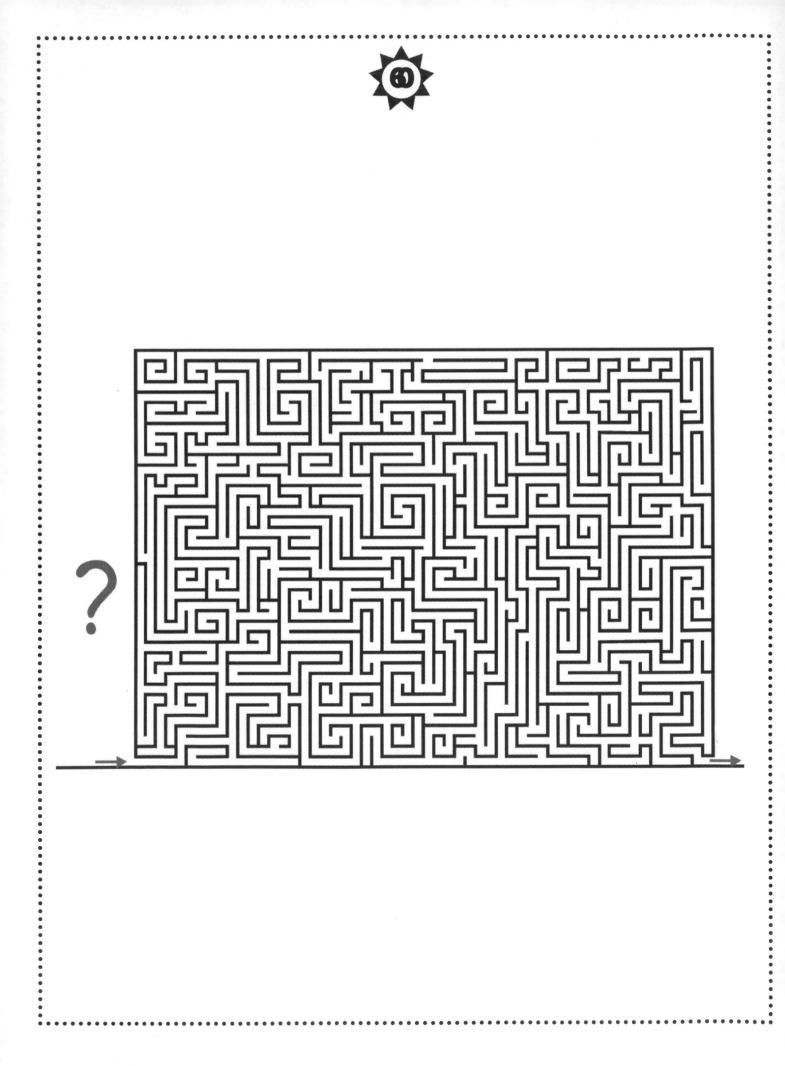

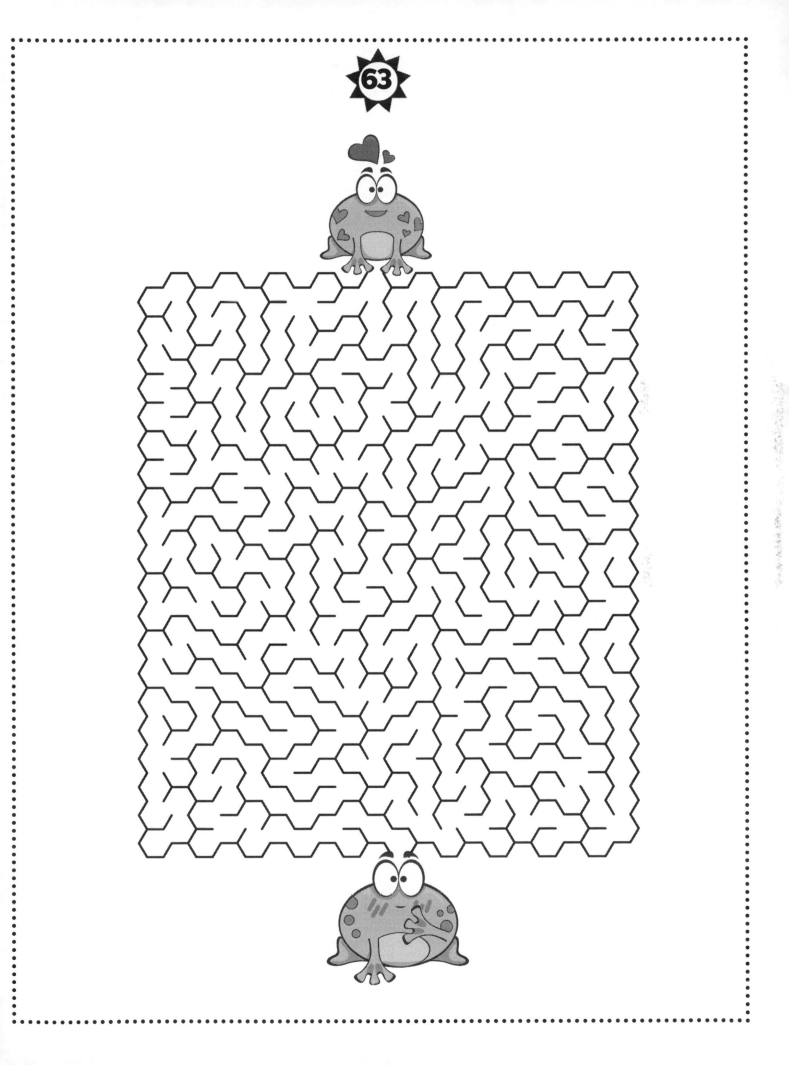

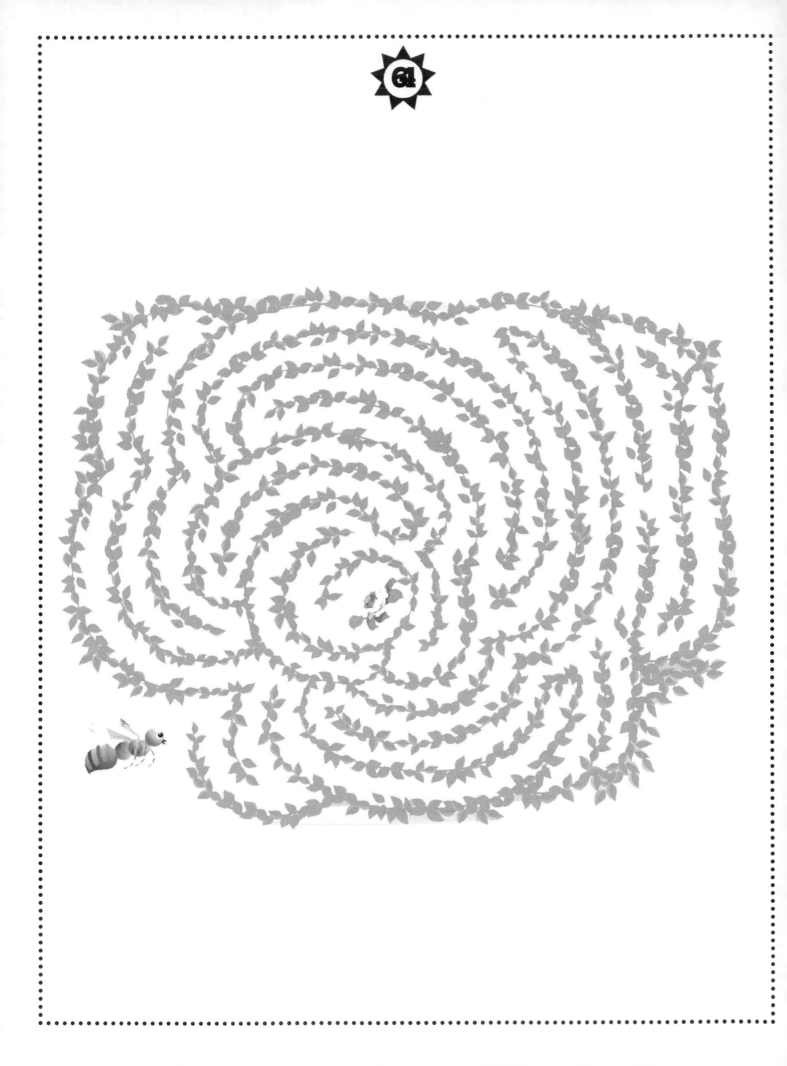

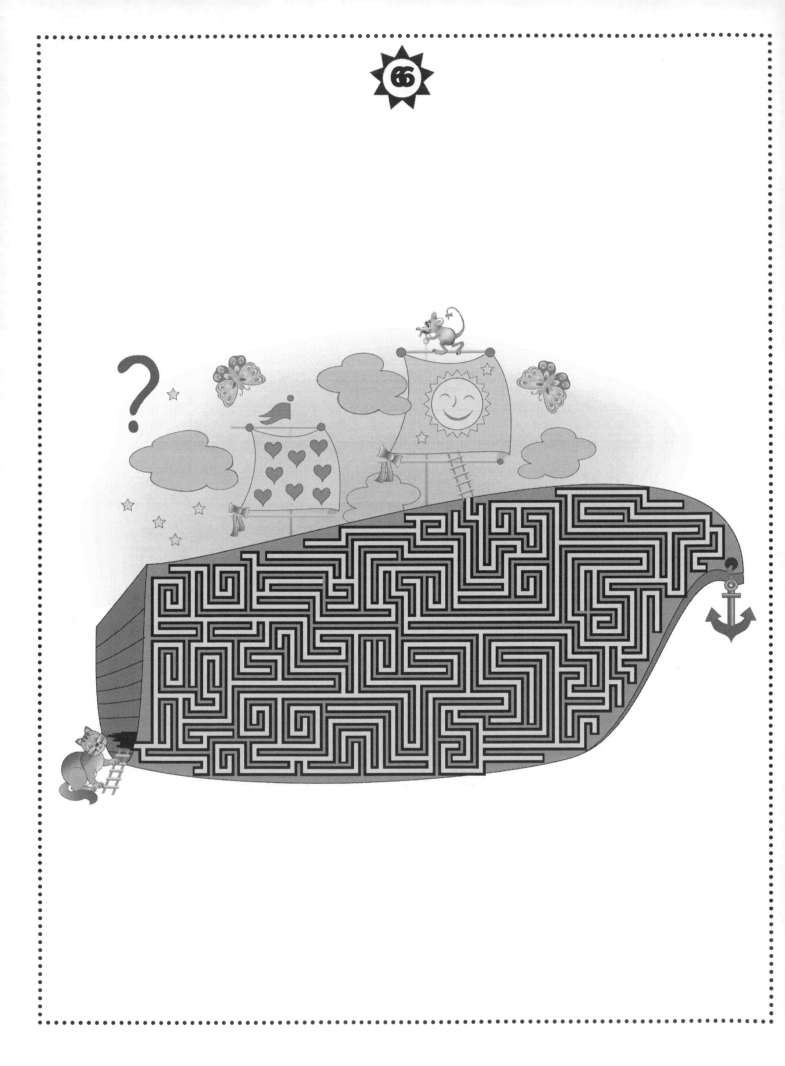

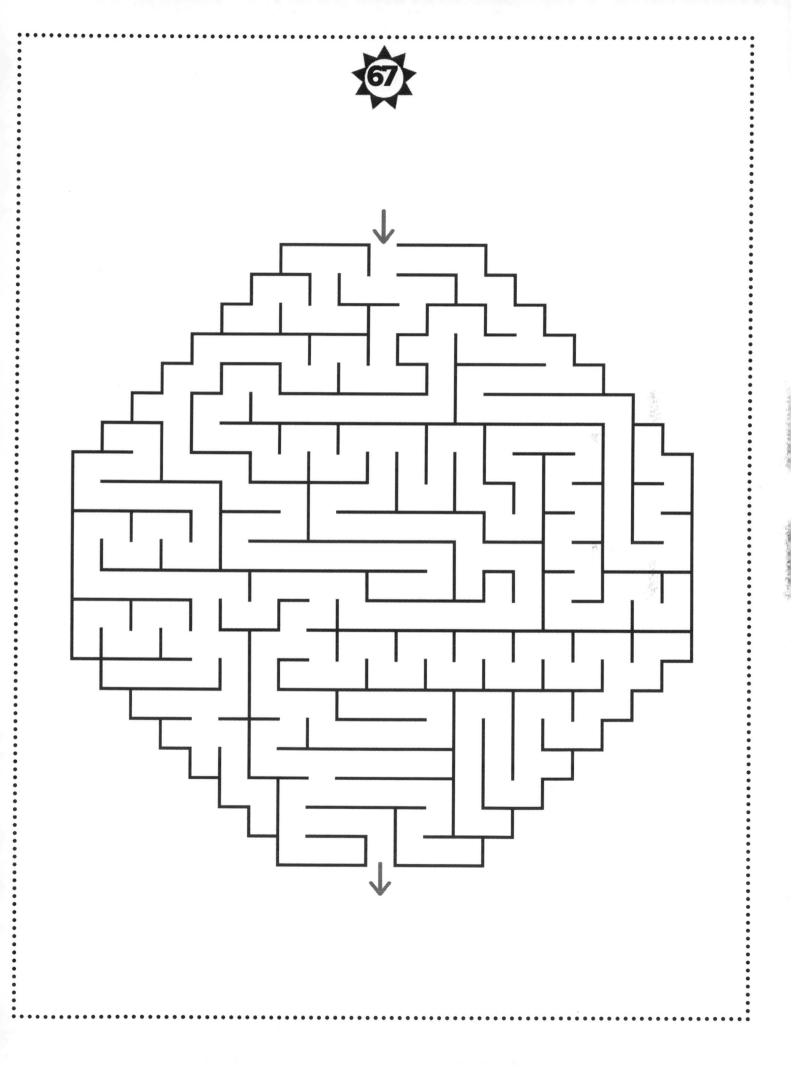

67

START

END

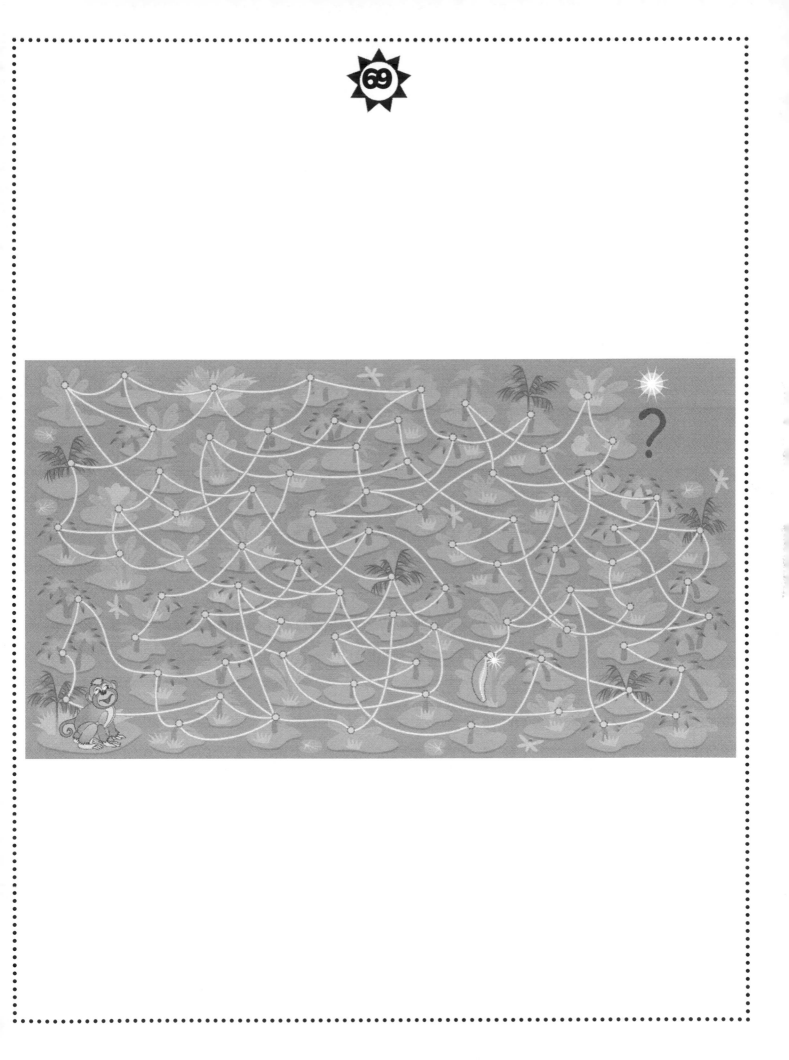

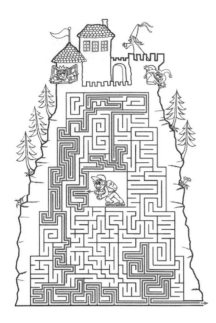

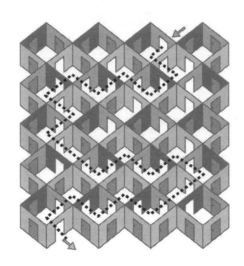

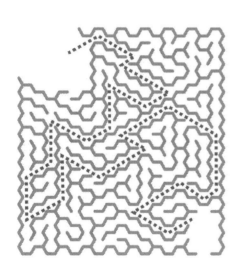

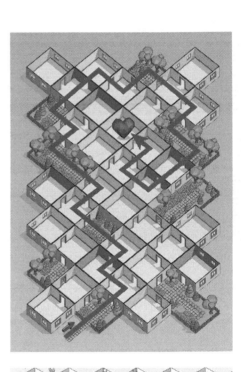

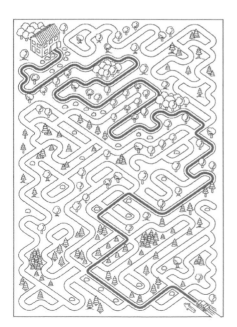

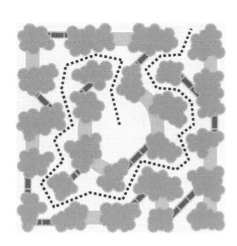

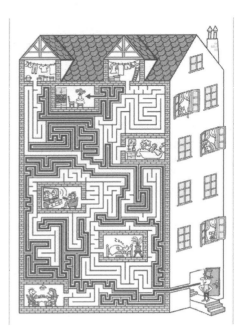

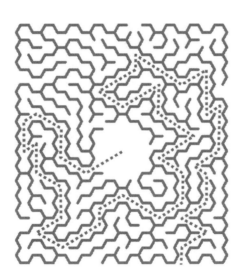

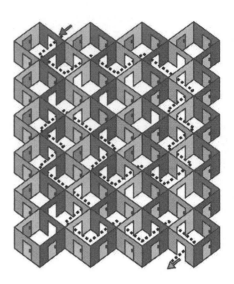

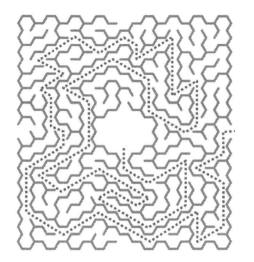

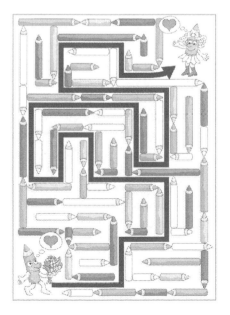

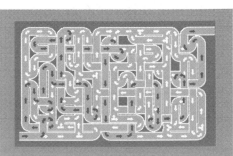

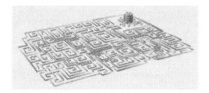

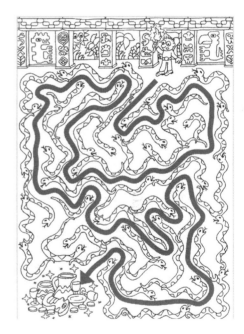

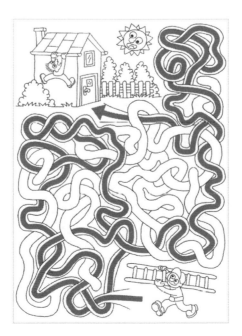

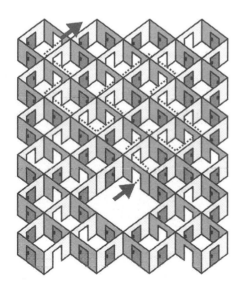

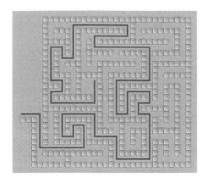

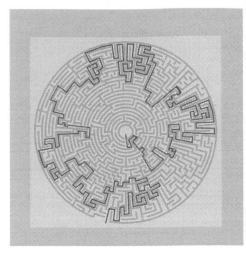

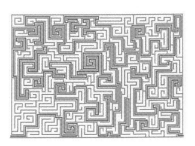

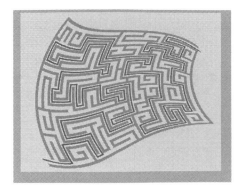

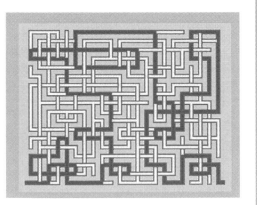

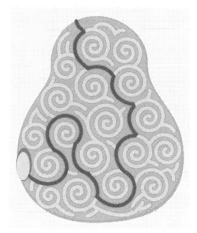

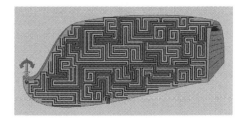

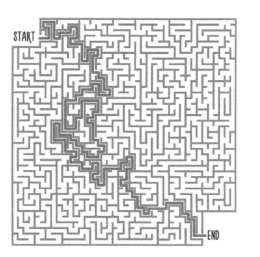

START

END

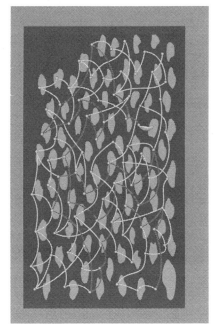

Made in the USA
Middletown, DE
03 June 2021

40961702R00044